Gold Stars

English

AGES 4 – 5

Written by Betty Root and Monica Hughes

p

Helping your child

◆ Remember that the activities in this book should be enjoyed by your child. Try to find a quiet place to work.

◆ Your child does not need to complete each page in one go. **Always stop before your child grows tired**, and come back to the same page another time.

◆ It is important to work through the pages in the right order because the activities do get progressively more difficult.

◆ The answers to the activities are on page 32.

◆ Always give your child lots of encouragement and praise.

◆ Remember that the gold stars and badges are a reward for effort as well as for achievement.

Illustrations by Simon Abbott
Design by Visual Image

This is a Parragon book
This edition published in 2002

Parragon
Queen Street House
4 Queen Street
BATH, BA1 1HE, UK

ISBN 0-75259-073-1
Printed in Malaysia

Contents

Beginning sounds

☆ Choose the right beginning sound and draw a circle round the right letter.

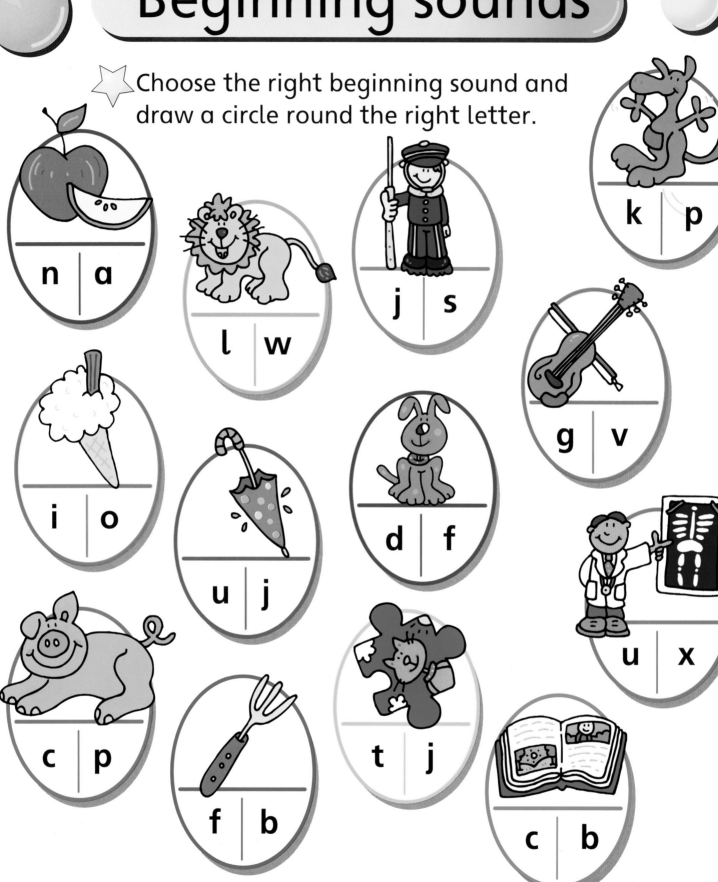

| n | a |

| l | w |

| j | s |

| k | p |

| i | o |

| u | j |

| d | f |

| g | v |

| c | p |

| f | b |

| t | j |

| u | x |

| c | b |

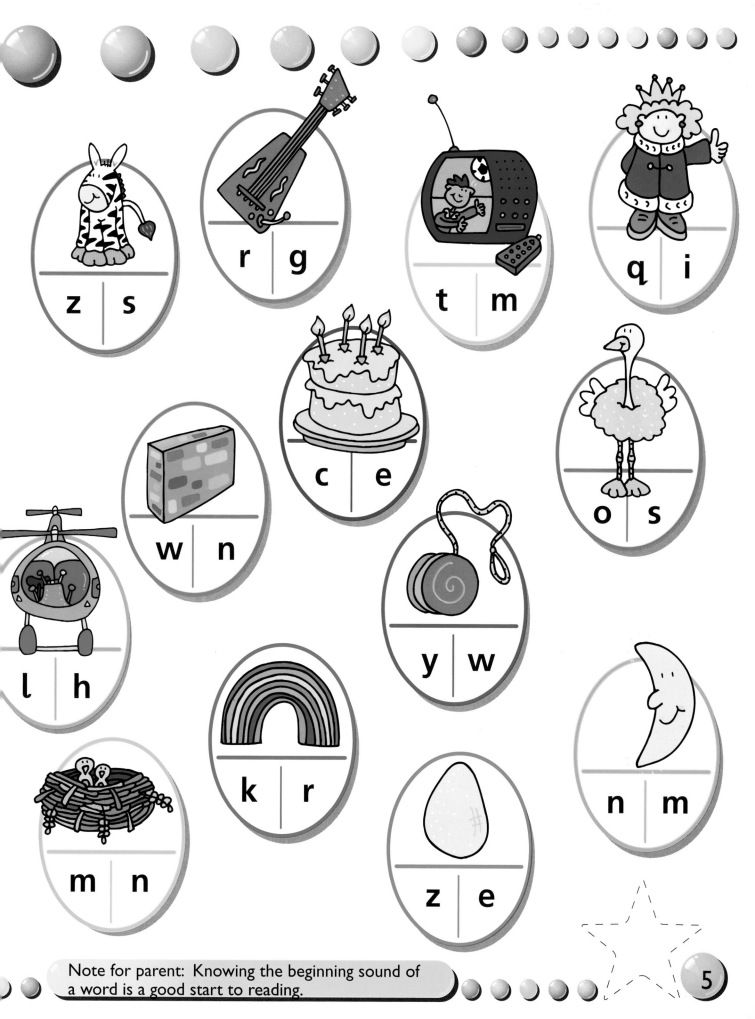

z | s

r | g

t | m

q | i

w | n

c | e

o | s

l | h

y | w

m | n

k | r

z | e

n | m

Note for parent: Knowing the beginning sound of a word is a good start to reading.

5

Colour the sounds

Colour the shapes below as follows:

h = red   c = blue   d = yellow   p = green

horse → h

cow → c

dog → d

pig → p

Follow the letters in the coloured shapes to match each animal with its baby.

Talk about

Talk about the picture. Read the words.

balloons

magician

cake

jelly

jug

oranges

sandwiches

pizza

table

dog

Find the rhymes

⭐ Draw circles round the two pictures in each line that rhyme.

Note for parent: Rhyming encourages children to listen carefully.

Sorting rhymes

Fill the empty squares in each column with the correct rhyming pictures. You can either write the name or draw the picture in the correct square.

Note for parent: Children will need to say these words clearly and out loud to complete this page.

9

Joining opposites

⭐ Read the words. Draw a line to join two pictures that are opposites. The words **cold** and **hot** are opposites.

empty

high

open

old

shut

full

new

low

Note for parent: This activity helps children to understand the meaning of 'opposite', and to know the right words.

big

dirty

fat

wet

sad

thin

small

happy

clean

dry

11

Completing words

Find the right letter from the row below
to complete each word.
Say each sound as you write it.

b s d c o j m t p

__elly

__andwich

__og

__izza

__alloon

__able

__agician

__range

__ake

Find the objects

 Look at the picture carefully.
Find 4 things that begin with the letter **b**.
Find 4 things that begin with the letter **p**.
Find 4 things that begin with the letter **d**.

b	b	b	b
p	p	p	p
d	d	d	d

Cross out a letter when you find each object.

Second chance

See what you can remember about beginning sounds and rhymes. Put a tick ✔ or a cross ✘ in each of the boxes below.

yes	✔

no	✘

begins with m ☐

begins with p ☐

begins with f ☐

begins with h ☐

begins with w ☐

begins with n ☐

rhymes with ☐

rhymes with ☐

rhymes with ☐

Note for parent: It is always helpful to give children a short test to see how much they have remembered. Let them look back through the pages of the book if they need to find the answers.

Find the mistakes

 There are five silly mistakes in this picture. Can you find them?

Find something in the picture that begins with each of these sounds:

c d p h w b

Rhyming pictures

Name the first picture in each row. Look at the other pictures in the same row. Put a ✔ by the one that rhymes with the first picture, and a ✗ by the one that does not rhyme.

Note for parent: Rhyming helps children to listen carefully in order to make judgements.

True or false?

 Look at the big picture. Read each sentence. Put a ✔ at the end if it is true, and a ✗ if it is false. The words and little pictures will help you to read the sentences.

tree

wall

cat

swing

girl

boy

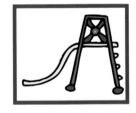

slide

1. A cat is up the tree. ___
2. A boy is on the wall. ___
3. A girl is on the swing. ___
4. A cat is on the wall. ___
5. A boy is on the slide. ___
6. A girl is up the tree. ___

Note for parent: This activity helps children to understand what they are seeing.

 Look at the big picture. Read each sentence. Put a ✔ at the end if it is true, and a ✘ if it is false. The words and little pictures will help you to read the sentences.

window

door

dog

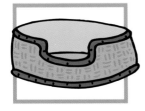

basket

Dad

Mum

sink

1. Dad is by the sink. ___
2. A dog is at the window. ___
3. Mum is by the sink. ___
4. A dog is in the basket. ___
5. Dad is in the basket. ___
6. Mum is at the door. ___

Word search

Look for each of the words below in the letter grid. Draw a ring around the word when you find it. Cross out the word from the list when you find it.

dad   girl   cow

horse   mum   boy   dog

baby   pig   cat

d	o	g	a	c	p	i	g
e	g	i	r	l	h	o	k
q	r	t	n	v	d	a	d
s	w	e	f	b	a	b	y
f	m	u	m	g	z	u	l
b	o	y	p	y	c	o	w
i	j	c	a	t	m	g	f
o	w	t	h	o	r	s	e

Make a story

⭐ Look at the four pictures below. Write the numbers 1 to 4 in the boxes to show their correct order. Start with number 1.

Find these things in the pictures:

socks

bed

T-shirt

orange juice

toothbrush

slippers

Note for parent: This activity encourages children to talk about the pictures and decide the correct sequence.

21

Second chance

⭐ See what you remember. Put a ✔ by the picture that rhymes with the first one in each row.

 ☐  ☐

 ☐  ☐

 ☐  ☐

Read the three sentences below.

   The cat is up the tree.

   The dog is in the basket.

   Mum is by the window.

22

Look and read

Look at each picture. Read the sentences below the pictures. Write the correct picture number beside each sentence.

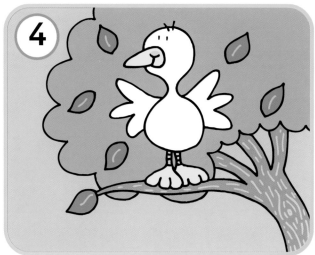

a. A bird is in the tree. ___

b. The girl is in the kitchen. ___

c. The boy is in the garden. ___

d. A cat is in the basket. ___

Ending sounds

⭐ Name each picture. Listen to the ending sound of each word. Cross out the picture in each row that has a different ending sound.

Note for parent: Children find it difficult to hear the last sound in a word, so they need lots of practice at this exercise.

Odd one out

Cross out the odd one out in each row.

or	or	of	or

it	is	it	it

at	am	at	at

no	no	of	no

am	we	we	we

of	of	of	on

Trace over the letters below. Read the words.

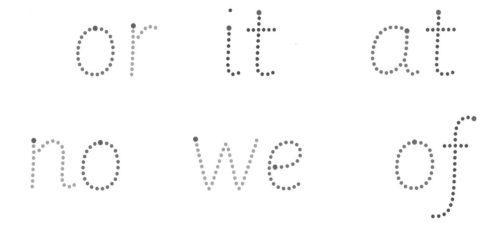

or   it   at

no   we   of

Note for parent: Children often read short words incorrectly.
This activity helps them to look at these words carefully.

⭐ Cross out the odd one out in each row.

is	is	it	is

at	am	am	am

on	or	on	on

to	to	to	of

up	up	no	up

in	is	in	in

Trace over the letters below. Read the words.

Sounds in the middle

Look at each picture and say the word. Write the correct middle sound in the empty space. Choose either **a** or **e** for the pictures on this page.

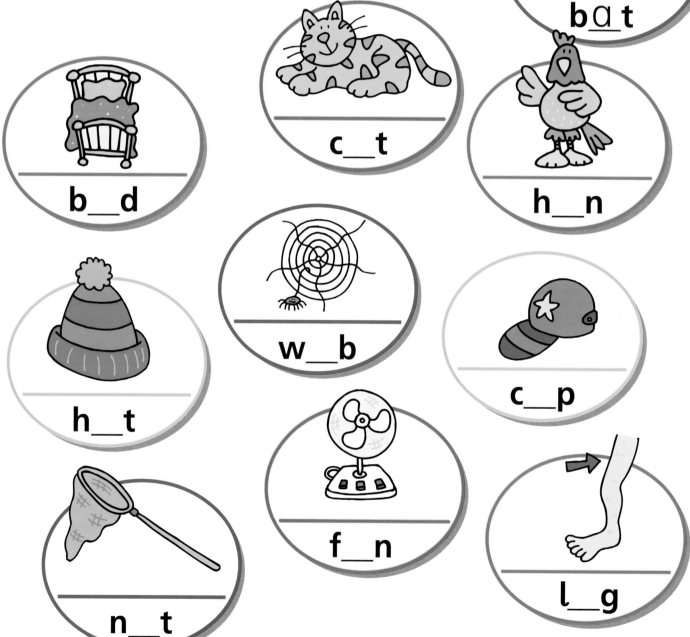

b <u>a</u> t

b__d

c__t

h__n

h__t

w__b

c__p

n__t

f__n

l__g

Choose either **i**, **o** or **u** to complete the words on this page.

p__g

l__g

s__n

b__x

j__g

p__n

b__s

s__x

d__g

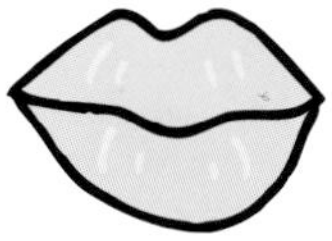

l__p

f__x

c__p

29

Double sounds

Name each picture. Listen to the sound at the beginning of each word. Cross out the picture that is the odd one out.

Match the sounds

⭐ Name each picture. Listen to the sounds at the beginning of the word. Circle the correct letters that match the sound.

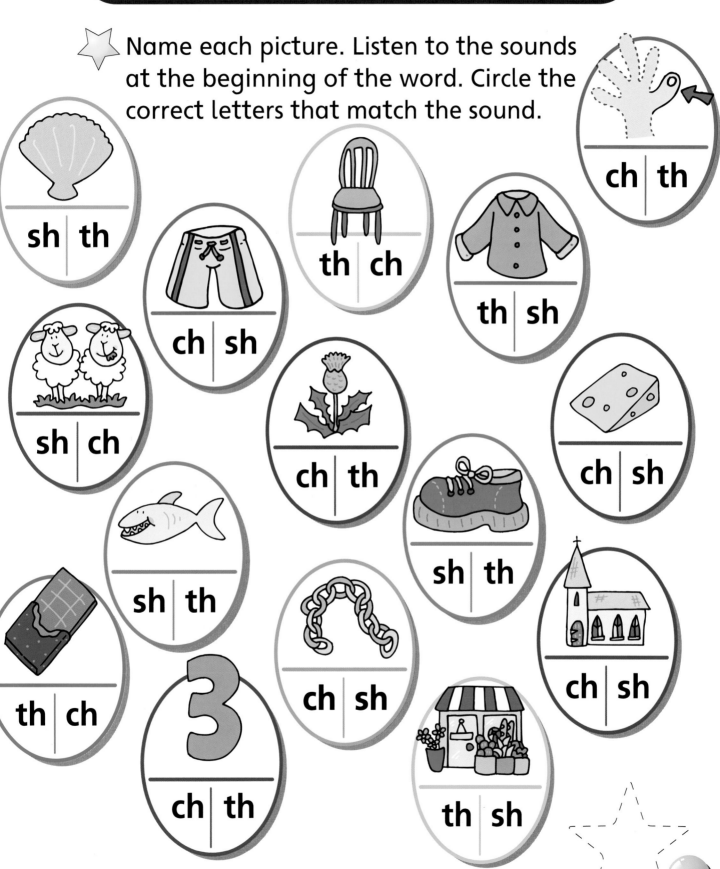

sh | th

ch | th

ch | sh

th | ch

th | sh

sh | ch

ch | th

ch | sh

sh | th

sh | th

th | ch

ch | th

ch | sh

sh | th

ch | sh

th | sh

31

Answers

Page 4
apple, lion, soldier, kangaroo,
ice cream, umbrella, dog, violin,
pig, fork, jigsaw, book, x-ray.

Page 5
zebra, guitar, television, queen,
wall, cake, ostrich, helicopter,
yo-yo, nest, rainbow, egg, moon.

Page 8
bat–cat, car–star, frog–dog,
clown–crown, three–bee.

Page 9
hat–bat–rat, fan–pan–man,
knee–key–bee, dog–frog–log.

Page 10
empty–full, high–low,
open–shut, old–new.

Page 11
big–small, dirty–clean, fat–thin,
wet–dry, sad–happy.

Page 12
jelly, sandwich, dog, pizza,
balloon, table, magician,
orange, cake.

Page 13
b: ball, book, bell, box;
p: piano, paint, pencil, puppet;
d: dinosaur, door, dice, doll.

Page 14
moon ✔, fork ✗, panda ✗,
helicopter ✔, watch ✔,
umbrella ✗, bat ✔, car ✗, frog ✔.

Page 15
The sheep is in the tree.
The pig has duck's feet.
The cow is in the house.
The horse is driving the tractor.
The dog is reading the book.
cow, dog, pig, horse, window,
book.

Page 16
ball–wall, car–star, fish–dish,
hen–pen, key–bee,
house–mouse.

Page 17
book–hook, sock–clock,
ring–king, moon–spoon, cat–hat,
door–four.

Page 18
A cat is up the tree. ✔
A boy is on the wall. ✗
A girl is on the swing. ✔
A cat is on the wall. ✔
A boy is on the slide. ✔
A girl is up the tree. ✗

Page 19
Dad is by the sink. ✔
A dog is at the window. ✗
Mum is by the sink. ✗
A dog is in the basket. ✔
Dad is in the basket. ✗
Mum is at the door. ✔

Page 20

d	o	g	a	c	p	i	g
e	g	i	r	l	h	o	k
q	r	t	n	v	d	a	d
s	w	e	f	b	a	b	y
f	m	u	m	g	z	u	l
b	o	y	p	y	c	o	w
i	j	c	a	t	m	g	f
o	w	t	h	o	r	s	e

Page 21
clockwise from top-left picture:
2, 4, 3, 1.

Page 22
fish–dish, key–bee,
house–mouse.

Page 23
a–4, b–1, c–2, d–3.

Page 24
These pictures should be crossed
out: bell, tent, cap, drum, flag,
clown.

Page 25
These pictures should be crossed
out: train, crab, zip, bus, five,
web.

Page 26
These words should be crossed
out: of, is, am, of, am, on.

Page 27
These words should be crossed
out: it, at, or, of, no, is.

Page 28
bed, cat, hen, hat, web, cap, net,
fan, leg.

Page 29
pig, log, sun, box, jug, pin, bus,
six, dog, lip, fox, cup.

Page 30
chair, cheese, chain – ~~three~~;
three, thistle, thumb – ~~sheep~~;
sheep, shell, shark – ~~thumb~~;
church, chocolate, chair – ~~shoe~~;
thimble, three, thumb – ~~shop~~;
shirt, sheep, shorts – ~~chair~~.

Page 31
shell, shorts, chair, shirt, thumb,
sheep, thistle, cheese, shark,
shoe, chocolate, chain, church,
three, shop.